Love The Lord
Matthew 22:37

A	W	I	T	H	V	M	I	L	G	G	Y
A	L	F	A	S	M	I	B	O	V	F	O
P	U	O	L	T	K	N	U	R	V	V	U
W	X	Z	V	H	Q	D	K	D	E	R	R
I	A	R	T	E	Y	H	E	A	R	T	P
T	L	J	C	T	O	H	W	F	T	C	K
H	L	Q	G	X	U	B	V	I	H	J	M
Z	Q	Y	O	U	R	I	S	D	T	C	G
A	G	B	D	E	R	Y	O	U	R	H	M
T	L	G	A	N	D	N	U	H	M	N	A
D	C	L	R	V	A	L	L	B	L	P	N
M	A	T	T	H	E	W	W	R	F	V	D

LOVE	WITH	WITH	WITH
THE	ALL	ALL	ALL
LORD	YOUR	YOUR	YOUR
YOUR	HEART	SOUL	MIND
GOD	AND	AND	MATTHEW

Love the Lord your Go̶̶   ̶   ̶   ̶   ̶ n all
your soul and with all   ̶   ̶   ̶   ̶   .37

1

Love One Another

K	K	O	U	N	N	N	H	G	T	S	A	L
L	A	S	P	I	U	H	M	D	Q	N	O
J	B	N	Y	F	X	F	U	C	E	O	V
L	J	Q	O	D	C	X	S	T	A	T	E
A	O	S	U	T	W	C	T	O	V	H	H
W	H	V	D	Y	H	Q	T	N	I	E	J
C	N	V	E	R	B	E	Z	E	C	R	M
C	L	T	A	D	O	N	R	X	T	Z	B
V	R	O	N	E	F	B	E	Z	R	U	H
E	I	Y	V	P	Z	V	M	L	O	T	T
W	Z	T	U	E	A	I	G	Y	A	Y	S
T	Y	P	S	H	Z	K	H	F	X	E	O

LOVE	HAVE	MUST
ONE	LOVED	LOVE
ANOTHER	YOU	ONE
AS	SO	ANOTHER
I	YOU	JOHN

Love one another. As I have loved you, so you must love one another.
– John 13:34

Rejoice!
Psalm 28:7

E	Q	V	A	B	C	S	D	F	E	G	H
T	S	P	R	O	P	M	N	L	D	K	J
I	Q	H	V	A	W	T	H	A	N	K	S
X	Y	Z	E	A	D	C	B	V	E	M	M
F	H	L	G	A	I	J	L	K	I	N	Y
S	V	W	T	U	R	S	Q	H	R	P	O
O	B	I	N	A	C	T	D	M	E	F	H
N	Q	P	M	O	L	K	L	J	I	J	G
G	S	U	T	V	W	A	X	O	Y	Z	I
G	E	F	O	R	S	D	C	Y	B	A	V
H	I	J	K	P	M	L	N	O	P	Q	E
V	A	N	D	U	T	S	W	I	L	L	R

MY	AND	TO
HEART	I	HIM
LEAPS	WILL	IN
FOR	GIVE	SONG
JOY	THANKS	PSALM

My heart leaps for joy and I will give thanks to him in song.
– Psalm 28:7

Be Exalted
Psalm 57:5

A	B	C	E	O	V	E	R	D	F	G	A
J	E	I	K	L	N	A	L	L	M	Q	B
Z	Y	X	W	V	U	S	R	T	B	P	D
E	A	B	A	E	C	E	D	L	E	T	C
A	M	O	B	L	K	J	M	I	H	F	T
R	N	P	O	Q	T	L	G	R	G	S	H
T	Z	X	V	W	A	E	O	U	L	T	E
H	Y	A	E	S	B	C	D	F	O	E	F
O	N	M	P	L	K	J	I	H	R	G	Y
P	Q	O	S	T	Y	O	U	R	Y	R	T
A	C	E	B	D	F	G	P	O	N	M	H
I	H	E	A	V	E	N	S	J	K	L	E

BE	THE	BE	PSALM
EXALTED	HEAVENS	OVER	
O	LET	ALL	
GOD	YOUR	THE	
ABOVE	GLORY	EARTH	

Be exalted, O God, above the heavens; let your glory be over all the earth.
– Psalm 57:5

The Plans Of The Lord

Psalm 33:11

T	H	R	O	U	G	H	A	O	F	B	A
O	F	E	M	L	O	R	D	D	O	C	L
F	G	R	P	S	A	L	M	H	R	I	L
R	I	Q	S	P	N	M	D	L	E	K	J
F	S	T	H	E	U	N	V	W	V	P	P
B	E	F	D	C	A	Z	Y	X	E	U	L
H	A	C	B	T	D	E	F	T	R	R	A
I	B	K	S	H	J	I	R	G	H	P	N
S	U	L	M	E	N	A	O	P	R	O	S
Y	T	H	E	X	E	W	U	V	T	S	Q
Z	A	C	B	H	D	E	G	F	I	E	J
G	E	N	E	R	A	T	I	O	N	S	K

BUT	LORD	PURPOSES	ALL
THE	STAND	OF	GENERATIONS
PLANS	FIRM	HIS	PSALM
OF	FOREVER	HEART	
THE	THE	THROUGH	

But the plans of the Lord stand firm forever, the purposes of his heart through all generations. – Psalm 33:11

God Loved The World

John 3:16

W	O	R	L	D	A	E	B	E	O	N	E
H	E	F	G	O	D	N	C	T	P	J	D
O	I	H	A	V	E	O	P	E	E	O	J
E	G	S	O	N	H	T	O	R	R	H	K
V	S	H	A	L	L	V	N	N	I	N	L
E	T	H	A	T	M	E	L	A	S	S	O
R	N	D	O	F	O	R	Y	L	H	P	V
R	N	S	T	U	E	V	I	W	L	H	E
A	B	A	E	V	Z	Y	L	Y	T	X	D
C	T	H	A	T	G	H	H	U	K	H	L
E	T	G	L	I	F	E	B	I	J	I	N
D	F	B	E	L	I	E	V	E	S	M	M

FOR	WORLD	ONE	WHOEVER	NOT	LIFE
GOD	THAT	AND	BELIEVES	PERISH	JOHN
SO	HE	ONLY	IN	BUT	
LOVED	GAVE	SON	HIM	HAVE	
THE	HIS	THAT	SHALL	ETERNAL	

For God so loved the world that he gave his one and only Son, that whoever believes in him shall not perish but have eternal life. – John 3:16

Grace Of God

A	G	B	H	A	V	E	C	I	S	E	T
Y	H	I	J	N	K	L	M	N	P	G	H
N	O	T	F	D	G	R	A	C	E	O	I
A	Z	U	Y	T	X	W	T	U	P	R	S
B	T	H	R	O	U	G	H	V	H	U	T
C	H	I	J	S	K	L	E	M	E	N	O
D	F	O	R	S	E	G	R	Q	S	O	F
S	A	V	E	D	T	L	O	L	I	P	R
D	I	T	U	B	Y	D	V	D	A	K	O
E	T	X	U	E	Y	O	F	E	N	J	M
G	H	W	V	E	A	C	U	I	S	H	I
F	G	O	J	N	Z	B	H	T	G	I	S

FOR	YOU	FAITH	YOURSELVES	OF
IT	HAVE	AND	IT	GOD
IS	BEEN	THIS	IS	EPHESIANS
BY	SAVED	NOT	THE	
GRACE	THROUGH	FROM	GIFT	

For it is by grace you have been saved, through faith– and this not from yourselves, it is the gift of God. – Ephesians 2:8

Salvation

Acts 4:12

A	S	A	V	E	D	B	O	I	S	G	F
E	A	U	F	G	W	E	D	N	C	I	O
H	L	I	N	J	K	H	L	M	E	V	U
T	V	S	R	D	Q	P	I	O	N	E	N
U	A	V	B	Y	E	W	X	C	Y	N	D
O	T	H	E	R	C	R	M	B	H	A	Z
F	I	H	E	D	N	G	H	U	I	J	T
N	O	M	E	N	T	A	C	T	S	L	O
F	N	V	U	A	S	Q	M	N	L	T	K
Z	O	Y	W	X	V	R	P	E	B	I	S
A	B	R	C	T	H	E	R	E	E	E	F
E	L	S	E	D	W	E	N	O	D	I	N

SALVATION	ONE	NO	GIVEN	WE
IS	ELSE	OTHER	TO	MUST
FOUND	FOR	NAME	MEN	BE
IN	THERE	UNDER	BY	SAVED
NO	IS	HEAVEN	WHICH	ACTS

Salvation is found in no one else, for there is no other name
under heaven given to men by which we must be saved. – Acts 4:12

Fruit Of The Spirit
Galatians 5:22-23

S	G	P	A	T	I	E	N	C	E	G	F
P	E	A	O	F	H	B	C	D	F	A	A
I	N	L	K	J	I	E	H	G	E	L	I
R	T	L	F	R	U	I	T	M	N	A	T
I	L	V	U	C	S	R	Q	P	O	T	H
T	E	A	Y	Z	O	X	W	A	B	I	F
G	N	G	O	O	D	N	E	S	S	A	U
P	E	A	C	E	F	E	T	D	C	N	L
H	S	I	H	J	K	L	M	R	N	S	N
Z	S	T	V	U	S	R	A	L	O	V	E
Y	X	J	O	Y	T	S	N	Q	P	L	S
B	U	T	W	K	I	N	D	N	E	S	S

BUT	SPIRIT	PATIENCE	AND
THE	IS	KINDNESS	SELF-CONTROL
FRUIT	LOVE	GOODNESS	GALATIANS
OF	JOY	FAITHFULNESS	
THE	PEACE	GENTLENESS	

But the fruit of the Spirit is love, joy, peace, patience, kindness, goodness, faithfulness, gentleness and self-control. – Galatians 5:22-23

Bread Of Life

John 6:35

I	A	A	M	B	C	I	N	E	G	F	N
N	B	R	E	A	D	K	J	H	O	G	E
P	Q	E	M	L	M	E	H	E	U	W	V
O	F	R	L	S	T	G	B	Z	Y	X	E
H	G	F	E	I	F	D	A	T	C	B	R
I	W	J	T	H	E	K	L	H	A	N	D
L	T	I	S	R	Q	V	N	I	P	O	M
I	W	U	L	N	E	V	E	R	V	W	C
F	C	H	B	L	A	Z	Y	S	X	I	O
E	D	J	O	E	F	M	E	T	G	L	M
M	L	K	H	U	N	G	R	Y	T	L	E
J	O	H	N	J	W	H	O	I	O	H	S

I	LIFE	ME	AND	ME	JOHN
AM	HE	WILL	HE	WILL	
THE	WHO	NEVER	WHO	NEVER	
BREAD	COMES	GO	BELIEVES	BE	
OF	TO	HUNGRY	IN	THIRSTY	

"I am the bread of life. He who comes to me will never go hungry, and he who believes in me will never be thirsty." – John 6:35

On Wings Like Eagles

Isaiah 40:31

S	A	I	N	O	N	O	T	T	C	D	B
W	T	K	A	N	D	H	U	H	O	P	E
E	W	R	U	N	J	B	I	O	E	G	F
A	H	N	E	A	G	L	E	S	N	Y	W
R	O	P	Q	N	R	S	A	E	O	W	I
Y	W	I	L	L	G	Y	H	N	T	A	N
L	Z	F	A	I	N	T	A	B	D	L	G
S	O	A	R	N	C	T	H	E	Y	K	S
W	L	R	E	N	E	W	H	D	F	L	W
I	I	P	D	G	R	O	W	E	L	G	I
L	K	I	S	A	I	A	H	I	I	H	L
L	E	T	H	E	Y	L	W	N	M	R	L

BUT	LORD	WILL	THEY	WEARY	BE
THOSE	WILL	SOAR	WILL	THEY	FAINT
WHO	RENEW	ON	RUN	WILL	ISAIAH
HOPE	THEIR	WINGS	AND	WALK	
IN	STRENGTH	LIKE	NOT	AND	
THE	THEY	EAGLES	GROW	NOT	

But those who hope in the Lord will renew their strength. They will soar on wings like eagles; they will run and not grow weary, they will walk and not be faint.

– Isaiah 40:31

Let The Little Children Come

C	A	E	B	V	A	S	C	D	S	H	K
J	H	K	L	M	I	M	E	F	A	I	I
T	Q	I	P	O	N	A	H	G	I	N	N
L	H	R	L	S	U	T	V	W	D	D	G
I	B	E	A	D	Z	T	H	E	X	E	D
T	O	C	S	F	R	H	N	Y	S	R	O
T	H	I	H	E	G	E	A	J	U	K	M
L	R	E	Q	P	V	W	N	O	C	N	L
E	N	T	M	A	U	V	D	F	H	X	C
Y	O	L	E	T	A	J	E	S	U	S	O
A	T	H	F	O	R	C	T	O	D	F	M
B	E	L	O	N	G	S	E	D	O	G	E

JESUS	CHILDREN	DO	THE	TO
SAID	COME	NOT	KINGDOM	SUCH
LET	TO	HINDER	OF	AS
THE	ME	THEM	HEAVEN	THESE
LITTLE	AND	FOR	BELONGS	MATTHEW

Jesus said, "Let the little children come to me, and do not hinder them for the kingdom of heaven belongs to such as these." – Matthew 19:14

12

No Eye Has Seen

I Corinthians 2:9

N	O	C	H	E	A	R	D	B	C	N	O
D	C	E	A	F	H	G	I	J	K	L	M
S	O	O	S	E	Y	E	R	Q	P	O	N
L	R	T	N	U	V	H	I	M	R	W	X
O	I	O	Y	C	Z	A	B	D	E	A	R
V	N	H	F	G	E	F	N	E	P	D	C
E	T	A	B	D	C	I	E	H	A	S	W
F	H	H	G	H	M	J	V	K	R	E	H
L	I	N	O	M	G	F	O	E	E	E	O
H	A	S	P	S	Q	O	R	S	D	N	T
U	N	V	W	X	E	R	D	Z	A	N	B
B	S	W	H	A	T	C	D	E	H	A	S

NO	EAR	HAS	PREPARED	HIM
EYE	HAS	CONCEIVED	FOR	CORINTHIANS
HAS	HEARD	WHAT	THOSE	
SEEN	NO	GOD	WHO	
NO	MIND	HAS	LOVE	

No eye has seen, no ear has heard, no mind has conceived what
God has prepared for those who love him. – I Corinthians 2:9

God Is The Creator
Psalm 19:1

T	H	E	A	B	O	F	C	D	T	E	D
H	P	J	K	Q	M	I	H	G	H	F	E
E	N	S	K	I	E	S	O	M	E	B	C
P	Q	T	A	R	S	U	V	W	X	Y	L
H	A	B	C	L	D	E	S	F	H	Z	A
G	A	H	I	J	M	N	K	L	I	M	R
U	T	N	S	R	E	Q	O	P	S	N	E
V	W	X	D	V	Y	G	Z	W	O	R	K
G	O	D	A	S	A	B	L	C	D	E	F
G	H	E	I	J	K	L	M	O	N	O	T
Q	H	R	S	T	F	U	V	X	R	P	H
W	Y	P	R	O	C	L	A	I	M	Y	E

THE	GLORY	SKIES	OF
HEAVENS	OF	PROCLAIM	HIS
DECLARE	GOD	THE	HANDS
THE	THE	WORK	PSALM

The heavens declare the glory of God; the skies proclaim the work of his hands.
– Psalm 19:1

14

The Lord Is Good

Psalm 13:5–6

S	A	B	U	T	G	O	O	D	I	C	S
A	E	F	G	N	H	W	I	L	L	J	I
L	O	R	D	M	F	L	M	E	F	K	N
V	N	O	P	H	E	A	R	T	Q	O	G
A	V	H	A	S	U	T	I	S	S	R	R
T	H	E	J	X	T	Y	E	L	Z	T	O
I	N	A	B	S	D	C	B	E	I	F	G
O	M	L	U	Y	I	K	E	J	I	N	H
N	O	R	Y	O	U	R	E	P	E	Q	G
X	T	W	J	U	V	U	N	V	T	S	R
Y	Z	E	C	R	B	T	O	V	C	I	N
I	R	F	P	S	A	L	M	D	E	M	Y

BUT	UNFAILING	IN	SING	HE	ME
I	LOVE	YOUR	TO	HAS	PSALM
TRUST	MY	SALVATION	THE	BEEN	
IN	HEART	I	LORD	GOOD	
YOUR	REJOICES	WILL	FOR	TO	

But I trust in your unfailing love; my heart rejoices in your salvation.
I will sing to the Lord, for he has been good to me. – Psalm 13:5–6

Serve The Lord

Joshua 24:15

A	D	E	G	B	U	T	M	O	P	Q	S
C	V	H	I	H	K	L	N	A	S	R	L
B	F	C	O	I	J	Y	W	U	E	S	O
W	I	L	L	U	Z	X	V	T	R	Q	R
E	K	L	M	D	S	N	O	P	V	M	D
X	Y	Z	J	I	B	E	H	G	E	F	E
W	V	U	T	S	J	E	H	D	G	C	V
N	O	P	Q	R	I	H	F	O	B	E	F
F	M	L	K	T	H	E	Q	G	L	D	C
A	O	X	W	T	S	R	N	B	H	D	K
Z	Y	R	V	U	M	Y	O	V	L	I	J
J	O	S	H	U	A	Q	P	Z	A	N	D

BUT	MY	THE
AS	HOUSEHOLD	LORD
FOR	WE	JOSHUA
ME	WILL	
AND	SERVE	

But as for me and my household,
we will serve the Lord. – Joshua 24:15

All Things Work For Good
Romans 8:28

O	F	R	B	A	N	D	H	L	M	N	E
W	E	O	E	C	K	H	I	S	P	S	C
A	K	M	E	C	R	Q	M	F	O	R	A
W	J	A	N	O	T	S	T	P	U	V	L
H	I	N	Y	R	X	H	R	W	T	O	L
O	H	S	Z	D	A	U	I	B	C	D	E
H	A	V	E	I	P	W	H	N	G	F	D
B	G	J	I	N	K	H	L	M	G	N	T
C	F	G	A	G	O	O	D	O	E	S	H
K	N	O	W	X	U	S	R	V	P	E	O
D	E	D	T	H	A	T	O	W	H	Q	S
W	O	R	K	S	A	L	L	T	H	A	E

AND	THINGS	OF	HAVE	PURPOSE
WE	GOD	THOSE	BEEN	ROMANS
KNOW	WORKS	WHO	CALLED	
THAT	FOR	LOVE	ACCORDING	
IN	THE	HIM	TO	
ALL	GOOD	WHO	HIS	

And we know that in all things God works for the good of those who love him, who have been called according to his purpose. – Romans 8:28

God's Love For Us

S	Q	D	B	H	I	S	C	D	W	E	C
T	K	E	J	I	L	H	R	G	H	F	H
I	L	M	N	L	P	O	Q	R	I	S	R
L	G	O	D	X	F	W	V	U	L	T	I
L	G	N	E	Y	Z	A	D	E	E	N	S
I	H	S	I	N	N	E	R	S	P	O	T
B	U	T	F	D	C	B	O	W	N	R	Q
J	K	R	L	I	N	M	M	T	S	U	S
Q	P	A	K	J	I	H	A	U	V	W	X
R	N	T	H	I	S	G	N	W	E	R	E
U	W	E	M	L	F	D	S	V	A	Z	Y
S	O	S	D	I	E	D	B	C	F	O	R

BUT	LOVE	WHILE	CHRIST
GOD	FOR	WE	DIED
DEMONSTRATES	US	WERE	FOR
HIS	IN	STILL	US
OWN	THIS	SINNERS	ROMANS

But God demonstrates his own love for us in this: While we were
still sinners, Christ died for us. – Romans 5:8

I Am The Way

John 14:6

S	T	U	V	T	H	E	W	A	X	O	T
I	C	F	D	E	R	X	A	N	Y	N	H
H	G	H	A	F	W	U	B	D	Z	E	E
I	J	K	L	T	V	U	T	O	P	R	S
A	A	M	V	C	H	M	N	H	Q	T	O
Z	B	R	M	D	N	E	X	C	E	P	T
Y	W	A	Y	H	B	V	R	K	J	A	H
W	X	E	O	T	H	E	C	D	E	N	R
V	U	J	G	O	A	Z	E	X	Y	D	O
T	H	E	P	N	J	F	W	M	E	U	U
S	I	J	R	M	I	P	Q	R	S	T	G
N	O	K	Q	L	L	C	O	M	E	S	H

I	THE	NO	FATHER
AM	TRUTH	ONE	EXCEPT
THE	AND	COMES	THROUGH
WAY	THE	TO	ME
AND	LIFE	THE	JOHN

I am the way and the truth and the life. No one comes to the Father except through me. – John 14:6

This Is Love

I John 4:10

B	U	T	A	B	I	W	E	T	F	S	L
V	T	H	I	S	H	M	N	K	J	I	O
C	H	D	E	F	G	E	L	H	E	N	V
M	A	I	S	Q	S	R	S	C	I	S	E
O	T	P	A	N	D	T	I	J	V	S	W
T	H	A	T	C	B	F	A	W	Y	S	X
D	E	O	U	R	I	F	D	H	N	O	T
G	K	N	O	R	L	E	K	N	I	N	H
O	P	Q	C	R	V	S	T	U	B	V	J
D	E	A	T	O	N	I	N	G	W	A	O
U	S	D	L	C	B	A	Z	Y	X	S	H
L	O	V	E	D	V	F	O	R	A	N	N

THIS	WE	HE	HIS	SACRIFICE
IS	LOVED	LOVED	SON	FOR
LOVE	GOD	US	AS	OUR
NOT	BUT	AND	AN	SINS
THAT	THAT	SENT	ATONING	JOHN

This is love: not that we loved God, but that he loved us and sent his Son as an atoning sacrifice for our sins. – I John 4:10

I Can Do Everything

Philippians 4:13

C	A	N	A	H	I	J	R	S	T	A	Q
B	C	H	I	M	U	Y	Z	O	B	P	V
H	D	G	F	W	X	E	H	D	O	C	T
B	C	I	J	D	V	W	F	N	A	E	H
J	E	G	K	L	K	L	M	G	I	H	R
K	E	V	E	R	Y	T	H	I	N	G	O
M	F	Q	M	P	O	N	L	V	Y	Z	U
F	G	H	N	Q	R	S	A	E	B	V	G
T	I	U	O	G	J	Z	E	S	C	D	H
K	T	S	T	R	E	N	G	T	H	P	Q
X	U	W	P	N	Y	T	U	W	X	S	R
P	H	I	L	I	P	P	I	A	N	S	A

I	THROUGH	ME
CAN	HIM	STRENGTH
DO	WHO	PHILIPPIANS
EVERYTHING	GIVES	

I can do everything through him who gives me strength. –Philippians 4:13

Go Into All The World
Mark 16:15

A	T	H	E	K	P	M	O	T	U	A	A		
R	W	S	X	L	Q	W	Y	N	Z	L	B		
C	R	E	A	T	I	O	N	I	M	L	K		
P	C	L	G	F	H	R	C	R	S	T	D		
N	L	P	Q	Z	Y	L	X	W	V	O	U		
A	B	C	D	F	G	D	E	J	O	H	I		
N	K	L	P	N	O	M	Q	G	R	S	U		
D	T	V	T	W	N	O	A	B	E	R	X		
H	O	K	J	H	X	Y	Z	R	F	Y	I		
D	M	L	P	R	E	A	C	H	K	Z	N		
E	H	D	F	G	P	Q	R	U	V	A	T		
F	G	E	N	E	W	S	S	N	C	B	O		

GO	AND	TO
INTO	PREACH	ALL
ALL	THE	CREATION
THE	GOOD	MARK
WORLD	NEWS	

Go into all the world and preach the good news
to all creation. – Mark 16:15

Give Thanks To The Lord
Psalm 107:1

A	B	E	Z	A	H	I	J	G	O	O	D
C	O	N	D	E	L	M	K	L	Z	Y	X
T	P	D	C	B	Q	O	P	N	M	H	A
H	S	U	F	G	R	D	R	C	V	I	B
A	R	R	S	T	G	E	F	D	H	S	I
N	Q	E	U	F	O	R	J	K	L	J	R
K	I	S	V	W	U	T	G	I	V	E	S
S	T	W	Y	X	V	N	O	P	V	Q	P
D	V	X	N	Z	Y	A	H	E	C	D	S
E	F	L	O	V	E	G	R	F	E	Q	A
I	G	J	M	I	H	O	T	L	N	M	L
T	H	E	K	L	F	J	K	W	U	V	M

GIVE	FOR	LOVE
THANKS	HE	ENDURES
TO	IS	FOREVER
THE	GOOD	PSALM
LORD	HIS	

Give thanks to the Lord, for he is good; his love endures forever. – Psalm 107:1

Do To Others
Luke 6:31

A	B	H	C	D	M	D	O	I	V	W	T
J	I	U	F	E	N	M	A	Z	Y	X	H
K	O	L	G	L	U	K	E	P	Q	R	E
Y	Q	R	S	I	J	N	O	R	T	S	M
O	H	F	O	T	H	E	R	S	U	B	O
P	D	G	E	D	C	V	M	L	S	A	Z
G	O	S	R	Y	T	N	T	O	T	U	Y
H	F	Z	Q	U	Y	V	W	Q	P	X	K
A	B	E	P	H	W	O	X	W	V	O	J
I	C	D	N	A	V	B	U	C	T	G	I
A	J	O	U	V	X	A	W	O	U	L	D
S	K	L	M	E	Y	Z	C	D	E	F	H

DO	WOULD	YOU
TO	HAVE	LUKE
OTHERS	THEM	
AS	DO	
YOU	TO	

Do to others as you would have them do to you. – Luke 6:31

H	E	B	T	H	E	G	Y	O	U	I	Y
C	A	N	D	C	L	O	R	D	J	G	O
Y	O	U	E	O	F	H	I	L	K	O	U
W	A	L	K	O	N	M	S	A	N	D	R
O	H	S	R	E	Q	U	I	R	E	Z	A
F	U	Q	H	P	J	U	S	T	L	Y	S
W	M	R	T	O	M	I	C	A	H	A	B
H	B	S	P	N	W	H	A	T	H	C	D
A	L	Q	T	L	M	E	K	J	E	T	G
T	Y	D	O	E	S	L	D	I	C	F	O
L	O	V	E	M	E	R	C	Y	H	T	O
M	A	N	A	N	D	W	I	T	H	G	D

HE	WHAT	THE	ACT	AND	GOD
HAS	IS	LORD	JUSTLY	TO	MICAH
SHOWED	GOOD	REQUIRE	AND	WALK	
YOU	AND	OF	TO	HUMBLY	
O	WHAT	YOU	LOVE	WITH	
MAN	DOES	TO	MERCY	YOUR	

He has showed you, O man, what is good. And what does the Lord require of you?
To act justly and to love mercy and to walk humbly with your God. – Micah 6:8

Give Thanks To The Lord
I Chronicles 16:8–9

```
W C A D A L L I H K N K
O H C M F G T T A L A N
N R K T O S O H S M T L
D O N H T N I E Q H I S
E N O A I H G N X M O F
R I W N A M E Z G A N P
F C N K G I V E Y K S R
U L C S S E G D H E I A
L E J T N T R G O J M I
C S C O W O N T N I L S
N A D Y L I U W H A T E
C A L L S H I S T E L L
```

GIVE	HIS	WHAT	SING	HIS
THANKS	NAME	HE	PRAISE	WONDERFUL
TO	MAKE	HAS	TO	ACTS
THE	KNOWN	DONE	HIM	CHRONICLES
LORD	AMONG	SING	TELL	
CALL	THE	TO	OF	
ON	NATIONS	HIM	ALL	

Give thanks to the Lord, call on his name;
make known among the nations what he has done.
Sing to him, sing praise to him; tell of all his wonderful acts. – I Chronicles 16:8 – 9

Share Your Faith
Philemon 1:6

I	A	T	H	A	T	B	Y	O	U	C	D	E
T	H	I	N	G	E	F	G	H	M	A	Y	T
H	O	I	J	V	K	T	M	O	Q	N	S	G
A	F	A	I	T	H	H	N	T	O	I	N	V
V	P	T	A	B	D	A	Z	M	R	I	W	X
E	C	E	W	C	F	T	E	H	R	I	J	K
A	E	V	E	R	Y	L	C	A	S	M	L	W
S	O	M	O	P	I	R	H	T	U	V	I	I
F	U	L	L	H	B	S	A	V	C	D	N	L
Y	O	U	P	Z	E	B	G	O	O	D	E	L
U	N	D	E	R	S	T	A	N	D	I	N	G
H	A	V	E	H	I	J	F	G	L	M	O	I
A	Y	P	R	A	Y	K	Y	O	U	R	P	N

I	ACTIVE	THAT	UNDERSTANDING	HAVE
PRAY	IN	YOU	OF	IN
THAT	SHARING	WILL	EVERY	CHRIST
YOU	YOUR	HAVE	GOOD	PHILEMON
MAY	FAITH	A	THING	
BE	SO	FULL	WE	

I pray that you may be active in sharing your faith, so that you will have a full understanding of every good thing we have in Christ. – Philemon 1:6

He Is Faithful

T	O	A	B	H	E	D	E	F	J	K	U	S
G	P	C	F	A	I	T	H	F	U	L	J	Y
Q	V	R	H	I	W	A	Z	J	K	P	L	L
R	U	H	O	Y	X	Q	S	P	L	G	O	N
S	T	I	I	F	O	R	T	O	N	E	D	D
P	H	O	H	H	E	G	U	I	M	E	C	W
Q	E	G	O	J	L	S	V	N	S	S	B	H
S	R	V	L	K	D	R	S	I	W	X	F	O
I	S	W	D	M	E	C	M	E	Z	Y	U	V
U	T	X	Z	W	A	O	R	T	F	E	X	W
L	L	K	S	J	R	B	G	S	G	W	E	Y
E	M	N	O	P	E	B	F	I	H	D	C	Z
T	U	N	R	H	E	C	H	O	P	E	B	A

LET	THE	HE	HEBREWS
US	HOPE	WHO	
HOLD	WE	PROMISED	
UNSWERVINGLY	PROFESS	IS	
TO	FOR	FAITHFUL	

Let us hold unswervingly to the hope we profess,
for he who promised is faithful. – Hebrews 10:23

He Is Mighty To Save

Zephaniah 3:17

G	O	D	W	B	C	D	W	L	O	R	D	T
R	A	D	G	I	Q	U	I	E	T	L	M	A
G	E	H	E	R	T	I	L	O	V	E	O	K
Z	O	J	R	L	E	H	L	Y	O	U	H	E
E	T	T	O	Z	I	A	C	D	E	T	U	I
P	U	X	Y	I	B	G	T	F	I	O	H	G
H	Y	O	U	L	C	Y	H	W	Y	L	N	I
A	W	H	N	V	T	E	F	T	L	I	S	S
N	I	E	U	H	H	D	E	I	G	I	N	H
I	L	S	G	T	S	C	W	N	H	J	L	E
A	L	I	I	Y	B	A	I	O	V	E	R	M
H	M	W	Y	O	U	S	V	H	Y	O	U	R
T	H	E	I	S	I	N	T	E	S	H	E	Q

THE	YOU	HE	YOU	HIS	YOU
LORD	HE	WILL	HE	LOVE	WITH
YOUR	IS	TAKE	WILL	HE	SINGING
GOD	MIGHTY	GREAT	QUIET	WILL	ZEPHANIAH
IS	TO	DELIGHT	YOU	REJOICE	
WITH	SAVE	IN	WITH	OVER	

The Lord your God is with you, he is mighty to save. He will take great delight in you, he will quiet you with his love, he will rejoice over you with singing.
– Zephaniah 3:17

My Heart Rejoices

```
T L I S R E J O I C E S I
H A I B O A S T S Z I B N
E B C F V V W X Y A C E D
M D F R T U E I O L O R D
Y E R S T E J R U H G F M
G O P Q L K D B R N O P Y
F D E L I V E R A N C E Q
L O Y L N M S A M U E L R
O M O U T H E N E M I E S
R J K N D E L I G H T O E
D I R M X Y A C F J M H P
H O N H I G H B G H T N Q
H E A R T Z M Y I K L I N
```

MY	IN	LIFTED	MY	YOUR
HEART	THE	HIGH	ENEMIES	DELIVERANCE
REJOICES	LORD	MY	FOR	SAMUEL
IN	MY	MOUTH	I	
THE	HORN	BOASTS	DELIGHT	
LORD	IS	OVER	IN	

My heart rejoices in the Lord; in the Lord my horn is lifted high. My mouth boasts over my enemies, for I delight in your deliverance. – 1 Samuel 2:1

A	J	P	L	M	F	O	R	P	Z	F	T	G
B	M	K	O	N	O	Q	T	R	E	N	H	I
C	D	Y	S	W	T	C	A	B	E	K	J	M
E	F	U	V	W	E	C	D	I	N	M	L	A
I	S	I	X	F	Y	R	C	Q	P	I	O	D
G	H	R	R	S	T	I	U	V	W	N	X	E
A	B	E	C	D	F	H	J	K	L	Z	Y	T
G	P	F	E	F	I	G	R	A	C	E	M	N
P	I	Q	U	R	S	D	E	F	H	S	O	Y
V	U	S	T	C	K	J	Q	G	R	T	U	O
W	Z	A	P	N	L	M	Y	E	D	W	V	U
X	C	O	R	I	N	T	H	I	A	N	S	B
F	O	R	W	E	A	K	N	E	S	S	Z	A

MY	YOU	MADE
GRACE	FOR	PERFECT
IS	MY	IN
SUFFICIENT	POWER	WEAKNESS
FOR	IS	CORINTHIANS

My grace is sufficient for you, for my power is made perfect in weakness.
– 2 Corinthians 12:9

Every Good And Perfect Gift

James 1:17

G	D	P	E	F	P	E	R	F	E	C	T	E
O	O	D	G	W	X	C	A	R	Z	B	L	V
O	W	H	O	Y	V	H	O	O	F	C	I	E
D	N	D	I	E	Q	A	G	M	P	D	K	R
B	C	U	H	J	S	N	H	F	I	I	E	Y
I	T	S	L	K	I	G	L	M	N	N	K	J
S	Q	R	M	T	R	E	R	Q	O	G	G	T
T	O	N	F	E	S	N	O	T	P	F	H	H
H	P	I	H	E	V	J	A	M	E	S	I	E
E	H	T	V	W	S	H	A	D	O	W	S	J
S	A	O	X	L	I	G	H	T	S	C	L	K
F	B	H	E	A	V	E	N	L	Y	B	M	N
A	N	D	Y	G	I	F	T	A	F	R	O	M

EVERY	IS	FROM	HEAVENLY	CHANGE
GOOD	FROM	THE	LIGHTS	LIKE
AND	ABOVE	FATHER	WHO	SHIFTING
PERFECT	COMING	OF	DOES	SHADOWS
GIFT	DOWN	THE	NOT	JAMES

Every good and perfect gift is from above, coming down from the Father
of the heavenly lights, who does not change like shifting shadows. – James 1:17

Answers

page 1 • Matthew 22:37

page 2 • John 13:34

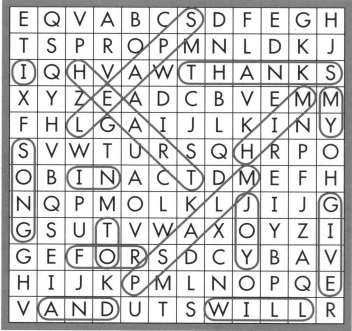

page 3 • Psalm 28:7

page 4 • Psalm 57:5

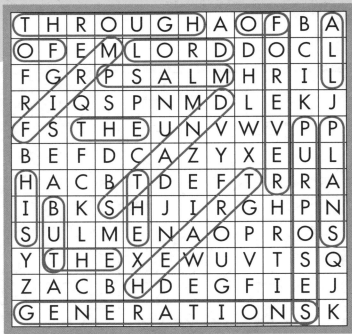

page 5 • Psalm 33:11

page 6 • John 3:16

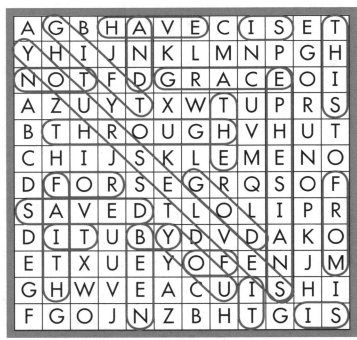

page 7 • Ephesians 2:8

page 8 • Acts 4:12

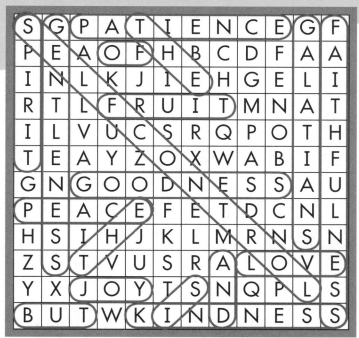

page 9 • Galatians 5:22-23

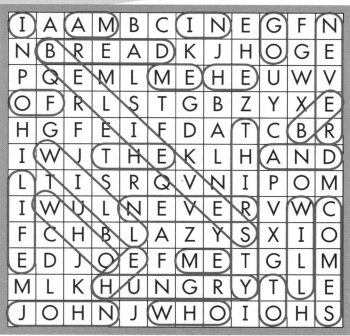

page 10 • John 6:35

page 11 • Isaiah 40:31

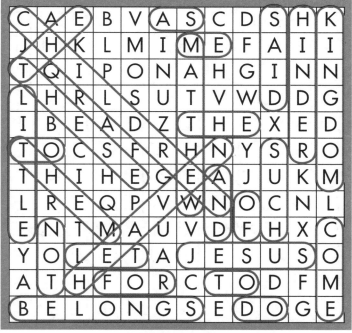

page 12 • Matthew 19:14

page 13 • I Corinthians 2:9

page 14 • Psalm 19:1

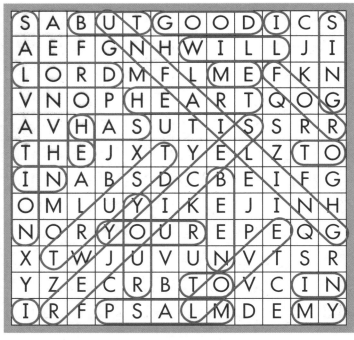

page 15 • Psalm 13:5–6

page 16 • Joshua 24:15

page 17 • Romans 8:28

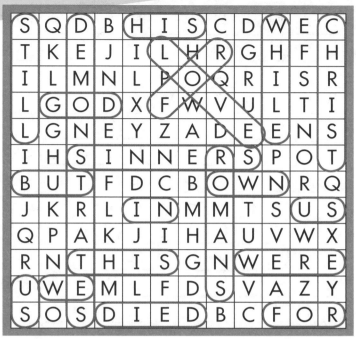

page 18 • Romans 5:8

page 19 • John 14:6

page 20 • I John 4:10

page 21 • Philippians 4:13

page 22 • Mark 16:15

page 23 • Psalm 107:1

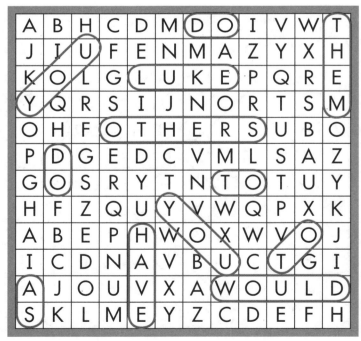

page 24 • Luke 6:31

page 25 • Micah 6:8

page 26 • I Chronicles 16:8–9

page 27 • Philemon 1:6

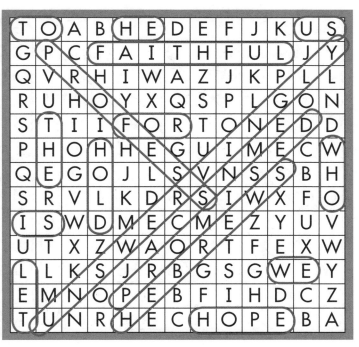

page 28 • Hebrews 10:23

page 29 • Zephaniah 3:17

page 30 • 1 Samuel 2:1

page 31 • 2 Corinthians 12:9

page 32 • James 1:17

Love the Lord your God with all your heart and with all your soul and with all your mind.

Matthew 22:37

Love one another. As I have loved you, so you must love one another.

John 13:34

My heart leaps for joy and I will give thanks to him in song.

Psalm 28:7

Be exalted, O God, above the heavens; let your glory be over all the earth.

Psalm 57:5

family fun:

Laminate the scripture cards at your local office supply store.
Display on your refrigerator and say the verse as a family during meal times.

But the plans of the Lord stand firm forever, the purposes of his heart through all generations.

Psalm 33:11

God so loved the world that he gave his one and only Son, that whoever believes in him shall not perish but have eternal life.

John 3:16

For it is by grace you have been saved, through faith— and this not from yourselves, it is the gift of God.

Ephesians 2:8

Salvation is found in no one else, for there is no other name under heaven given to men by which we must be saved.

Acts 4:12

But the fruit of the Spirit is love, joy, peace, patience, kindness, goodness, faithfulness, gentleness and self-control.

Galatians 5:22-23

"I am the bread of life. He who comes to me will never go hungry, and he who believes in me will never be thirsty."

John 6:35

But those who hope in the Lord will renew their strength. They will soar on wings like eagles; they will run and not grow weary, they will walk and not be faint.

Isaiah 40:31

Jesus said, "Let the little children come to me, and do not hinder them, for the kingdom of heaven belongs to such as these."

Matthew 19:14

family fun:

Do a family devotion on one of the verses. Read the story from the Bible and discuss what the verse means. Discuss how the verse applies to your life today.

No eye has seen, no ear has heard, no mind has conceived what God has prepared for those who love him.

1 Corinthians 2:9

The heavens declare the glory of God; the skies proclaim the work of his hands.

Psalm 19:1

But I trust in your unfailing love; my heart rejoices in your salvation. I will sing to the Lord, for he has been good to me.

Psalm 13:5-6

But as for me and my household, we will serve the Lord.

Joshua 24:15

And we know that in all things God works for the good of those who love him, who have been called according to his purpose.

Romans 8:28

But God demonstrates his own love for us in this: While we were still sinners, Christ died for us.

Romans 5:8

I am the way and the truth and the life. No one comes to the Father except through me.

John 14:6

This is love: not that we loved God, but that he loved us and sent his Son as an atoning sacrifice for our sins.

1 John 4:10

family fun:

Read Psalm 107:1, then make an "I Am Thankful" list. This is a perfect "at the dinner table" activity. Go around the table and have everyone tell one thing they are thankful for each day.

I can do everything through him
who gives me strength.

Philippians 4:13

Go into all the world and preach the
good news to all creation.

Mark 16:15

Give thanks to the Lord, for he is good;
his love endures forever.

Psalm 107:1

Do to others as you would have them do to you.

Luke 6:31

He has showed you, O man, what is good.
And what does the Lord require of you? To act justly
and to love mercy and to walk humbly with your God.

Micah 6:8

Give thanks to the Lord, call on his name; make known
among the nations what he has done. Sing to him,
sing praise to him; tell of all his wonderful acts.

1 Chronicles 16:8-9

I pray that you may be active in sharing your
faith, so that you will have a full understanding
of every good thing we have in Christ.

Philemon 1:6

Let us hold unswervingly to the hope we
profess, for he who promised is faithful.

Hebrews 10:23

family fun:

Read Matthew 10:2-4 to learn the names of Jesus' twelve Apostles. Download the song "The Twelve Apostles" and memorize their names. Learning with music is easy and a fun way to memorize facts!

The Lord your God is with you, he is mighty to save. He will take great delight in you, he will quiet you with his love, he will rejoice over you with singing.

Zephaniah 3:17

My heart rejoices in the Lord; In the Lord my horn is lifted high. My mouth boasts over my enemies, for I delight in your deliverance.

1 Samuel 2:1

My grace is sufficient for you, for my power is made perfect in weakness.

2 Corinthians 12:9

Every good and perfect gift is from above, coming down from the Father of the heavenly lights, who does not change like shifting shadows.

James 1:17